Ready-to-Make
PHOTO & SCENE MACHINES

ANTIQUE
OPTICAL INVENTIONS
• Recreated •

By BUDD WENTZ

Troubador Press San Francisco

ABOUT THIS BOOK

There's a lot more to the history of photography than just cameras. A whole variety of wild contraptions invented by madmen, magicians, artists, priests and just plain inventors grew out of the great quest for "painting with light," as photography was once called.

With pages from this book, scissors, tape, glue and a few odds and ends from around your home, you can recreate each of these historic optical inventions that are the cousins and ancestors of today's camera. All the devices built from this book actually work. Project dazzling scenes with a magic lantern slide projector. View the world upside down through an antique-style camera, as well as use it to take pictures. Produce kaleidoscopic reflections, 3-D images, anamorphic illusions and other surprising sights.

Some of the projects are a little more complicated than others, so browse through the book to find one that suits you for starting out. When you've finished all ten inventions, you'll have a great collection of old-time favorites for entertaining guests in your parlor. Then see if you can dream up an invention on your own.

MATERIALS NEEDED

Plastic tape	Tracing paper	Ruler
White glue	Clear plastic wrap	Magnifying glass
Pencils	Paper fastener	Purse-size mirrors
Scissors	Spool	Photo paper (optional)

Flashlight or Small desk lamp

Published in the United States of America by Troubador Press, 385 Fremont Street, San Francisco, CA 94105. ISBN: 0-912300-83-3

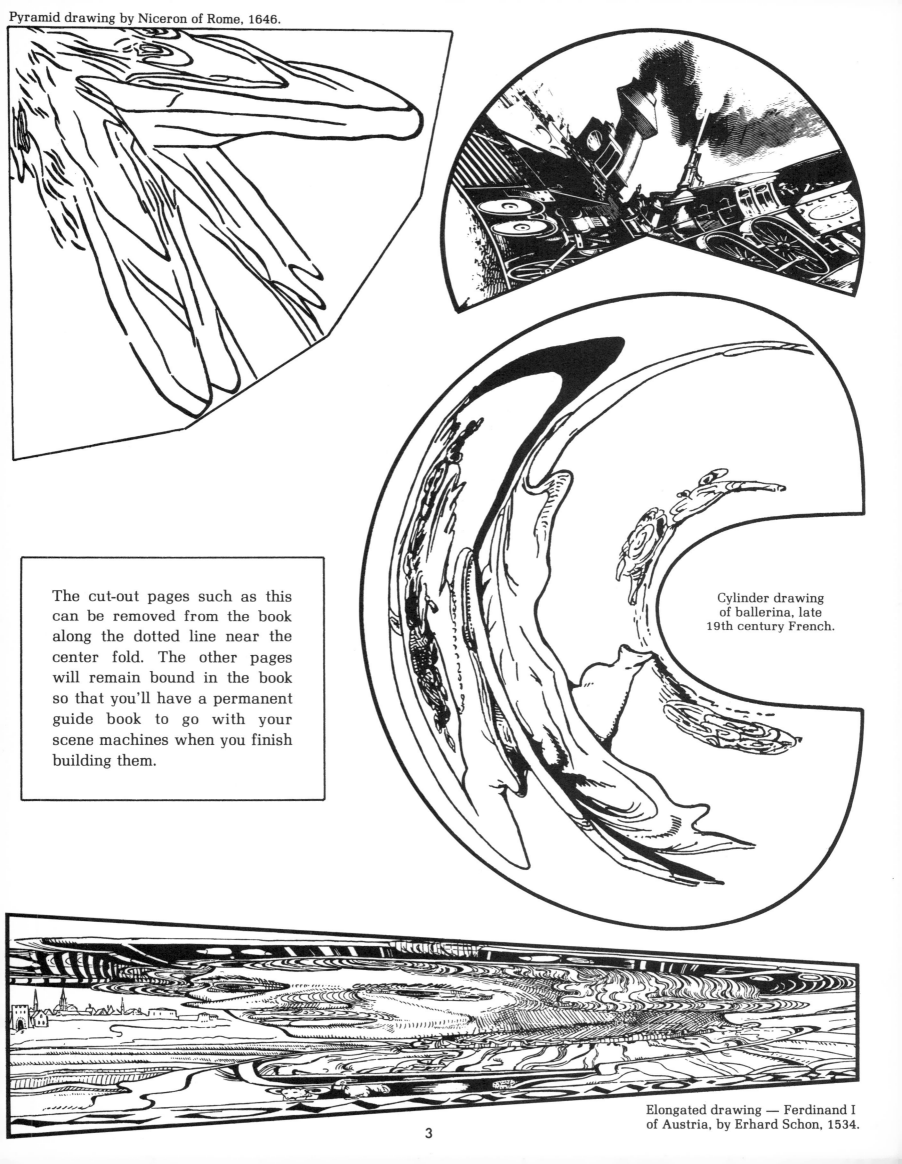

Pyramid drawing by Niceron of Rome, 1646.

Cylinder drawing
of ballerina, late
19th century French.

The cut-out pages such as this can be removed from the book along the dotted line near the center fold. The other pages will remain bound in the book so that you'll have a permanent guide book to go with your scene machines when you finish building them.

Elongated drawing — Ferdinand I
of Austria, by Erhard Schon, 1534.

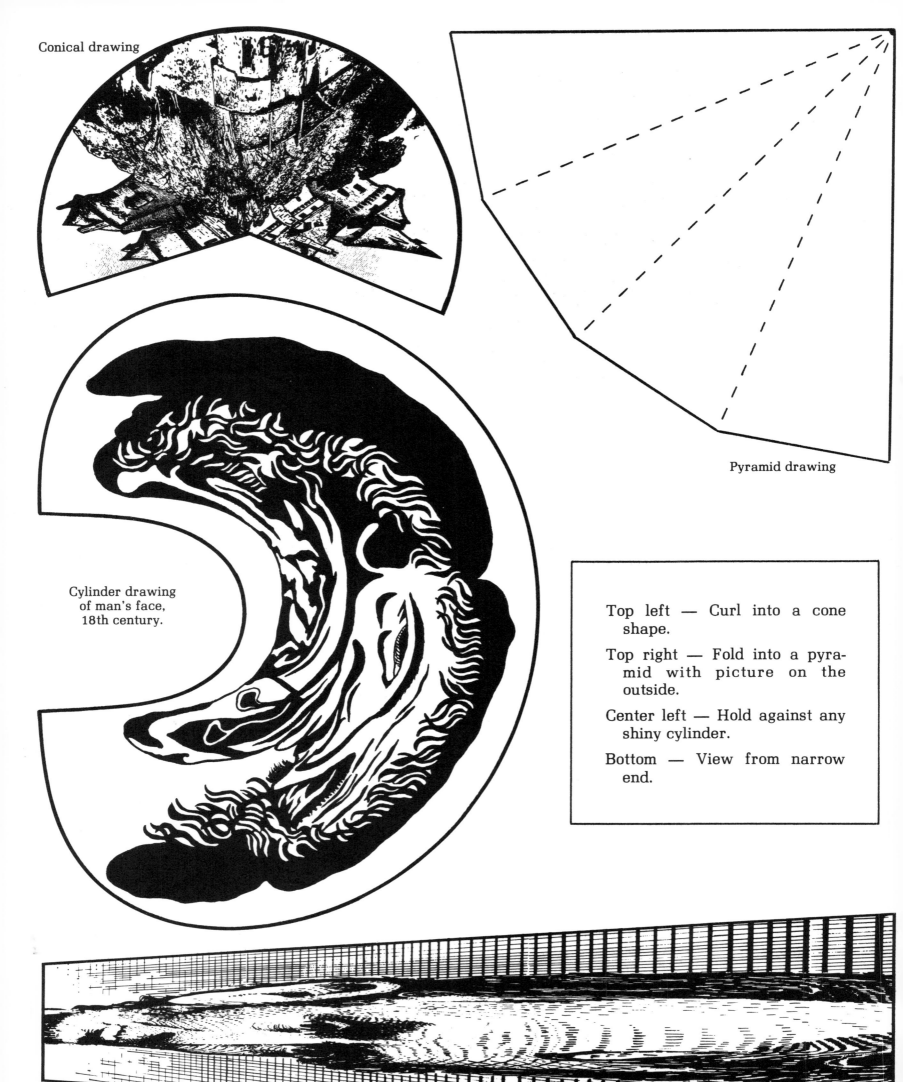

Conical drawing

Pyramid drawing

Cylinder drawing
of man's face,
18th century.

Top left — Curl into a cone shape.

Top right — Fold into a pyramid with picture on the outside.

Center left — Hold against any shiny cylinder.

Bottom — View from narrow end.

Elongated drawing — Abraham Lincoln.
(courtesy of Ontario Science Center, Toronto)

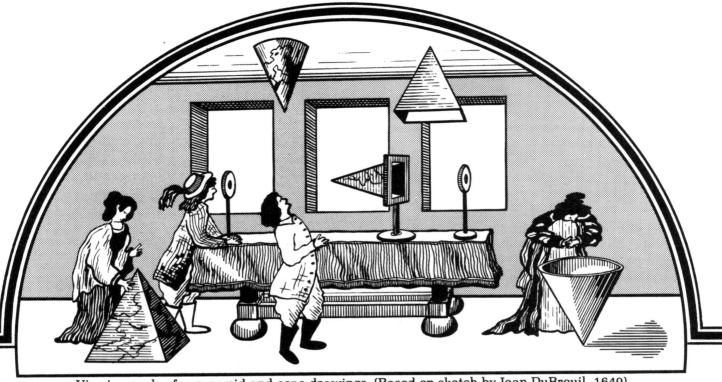

Viewing parlor for pyramid and cone drawings. (Based on sketch by Jean DuBreuil, 1649)

ANAMORPHIC PICTURES

ANAMORPHIC picture devices were as popular 300 years ago as fun-house mirrors are today, except that they work in reverse. These strangely distorted drawings look normal only by observing them in just the right way.

Samples of the parlor game pictured on this page are provided in cut-out form on pages 3 and 4. Your specially-shaped cylinder drawings can be viewed by holding them against any shiny cylinder such as: a chromed drain pipe, toilet paper holder or towel rod; aluminized plastic cup; brass pole lamp; smooth shiny flashlight; chrome table or chair leg.

Painters sometimes used ANAMORPHIC drawings to sneak political or religious messages into their artworks. For example, a Hans Holbein painting of 1533 shows a skull floating mysteriously at the feet of two powerful leaders of that time, but the skull can only be seen when viewed from one corner of the picture. This style has even been used to conceal indelicate pictures in otherwise innocent looking artworks.

Cylinder drawing and reflective viewer. (Universal City Studios collection)

Viewing an elongated drawing.

5

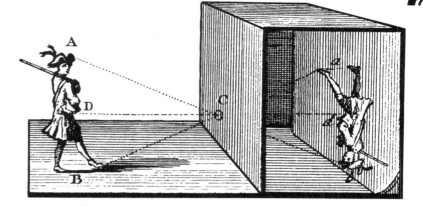

CAMERA OBSCURA

One of the oldest scene machines is the CAMERA OBSCURA, meaning "dark chamber." If a tiny hole is drilled in the wall of a darkened room, a faint upside down picture of any scenery outside will be projected onto the opposite wall. You can make your own portable version of this contraption using the cut-outs on page 7.

Aristotle of ancient Greece may have known about the CAMERA OBSCURA, and at least a thousand years ago it was used by Arabian astronomers to watch eclipses of the sun. When a lens was added, around 1568, this greatly improved model soon became a favorite tool among artists for tracing scenery.

Some people feared these magic boxes as the work of evil spirits, and on one occasion a traveling artist used his CAMERA OBSCURA to frighten away a high government official who was trying to get bribes from him.

19th century CAMERA OBSCURA for sketching. (Bingham Museum of Photography, University of California at Riverside, photo by Kleinman)

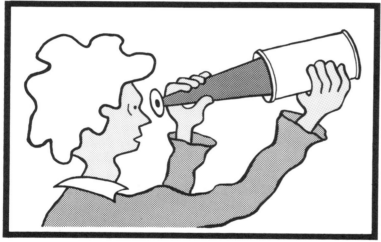

Your CAMERA OBSCURA in use.

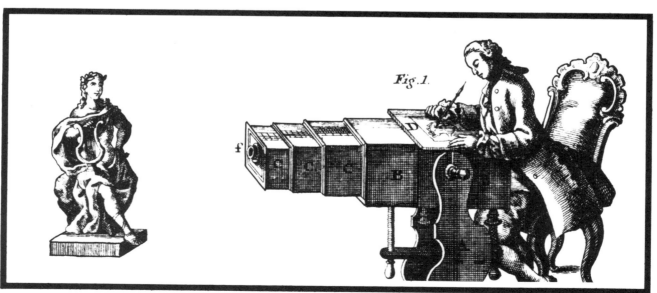

TELESCOPING CAMERA OBSCURA, 1769. (Gernsheim collection, University of Texas at Austin, Humanities Research Center)

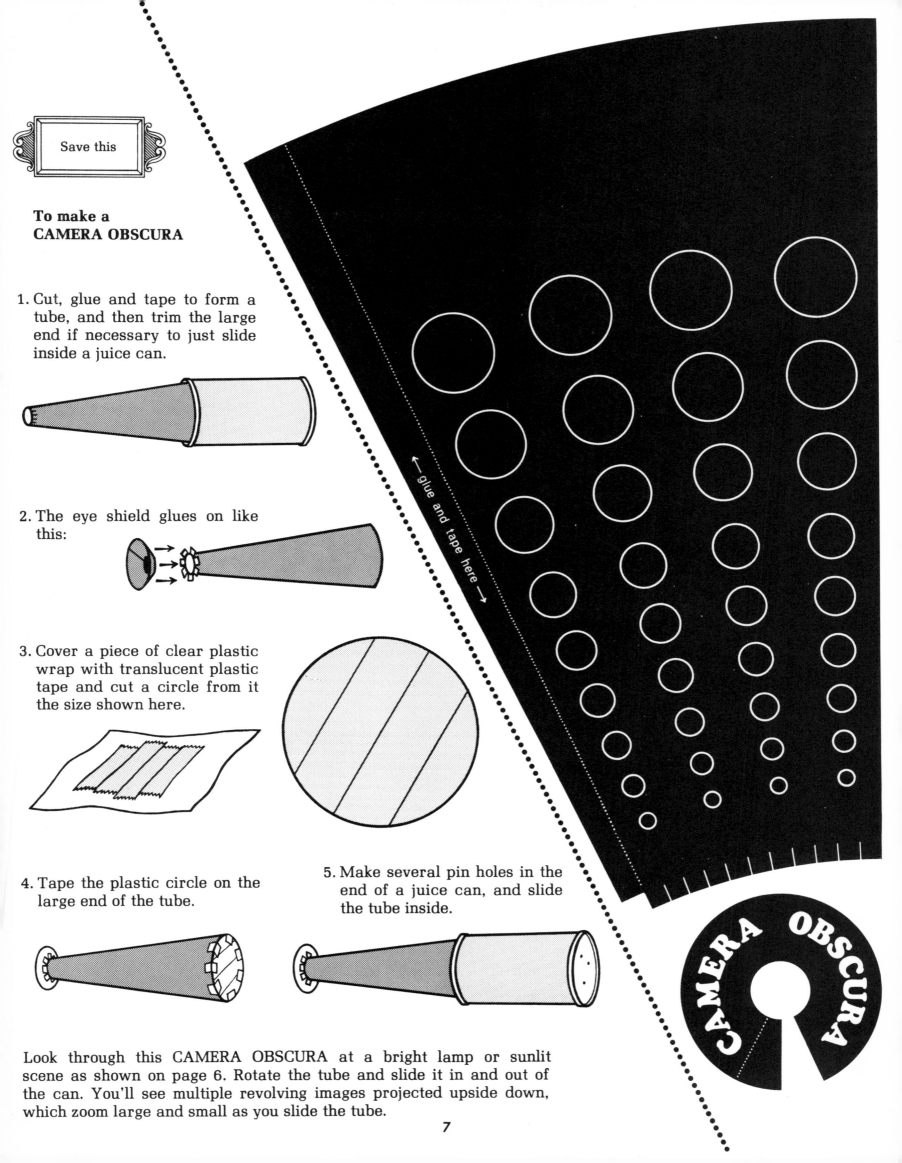

**To make a
CAMERA OBSCURA**

1. Cut, glue and tape to form a tube, and then trim the large end if necessary to just slide inside a juice can.

2. The eye shield glues on like this:

3. Cover a piece of clear plastic wrap with translucent plastic tape and cut a circle from it the size shown here.

4. Tape the plastic circle on the large end of the tube.

5. Make several pin holes in the end of a juice can, and slide the tube inside.

← glue and tape here →

CAMERA OBSCURA

Look through this CAMERA OBSCURA at a bright lamp or sunlit scene as shown on page 6. Rotate the tube and slide it in and out of the can. You'll see multiple revolving images projected upside down, which zoom large and small as you slide the tube.

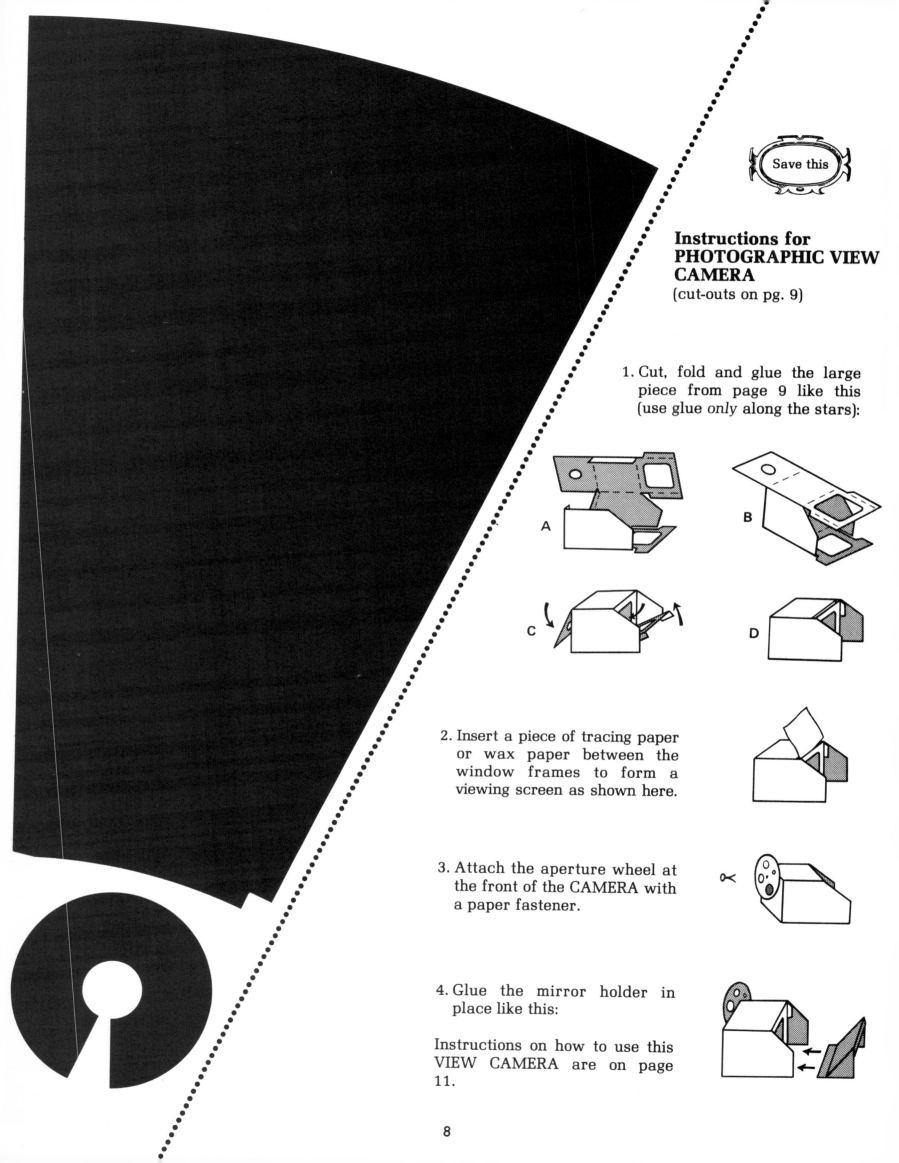

Save this

Instructions for
PHOTOGRAPHIC VIEW
CAMERA
(cut-outs on pg. 9)

1. Cut, fold and glue the large
   piece from page 9 like this
   (use glue *only* along the stars):

A

B

C

D

2. Insert a piece of tracing paper
   or wax paper between the
   window frames to form a
   viewing screen as shown here.

3. Attach the aperture wheel at
   the front of the CAMERA with
   a paper fastener.

4. Glue the mirror holder in
   place like this:

Instructions on how to use this
VIEW CAMERA are on page
11.

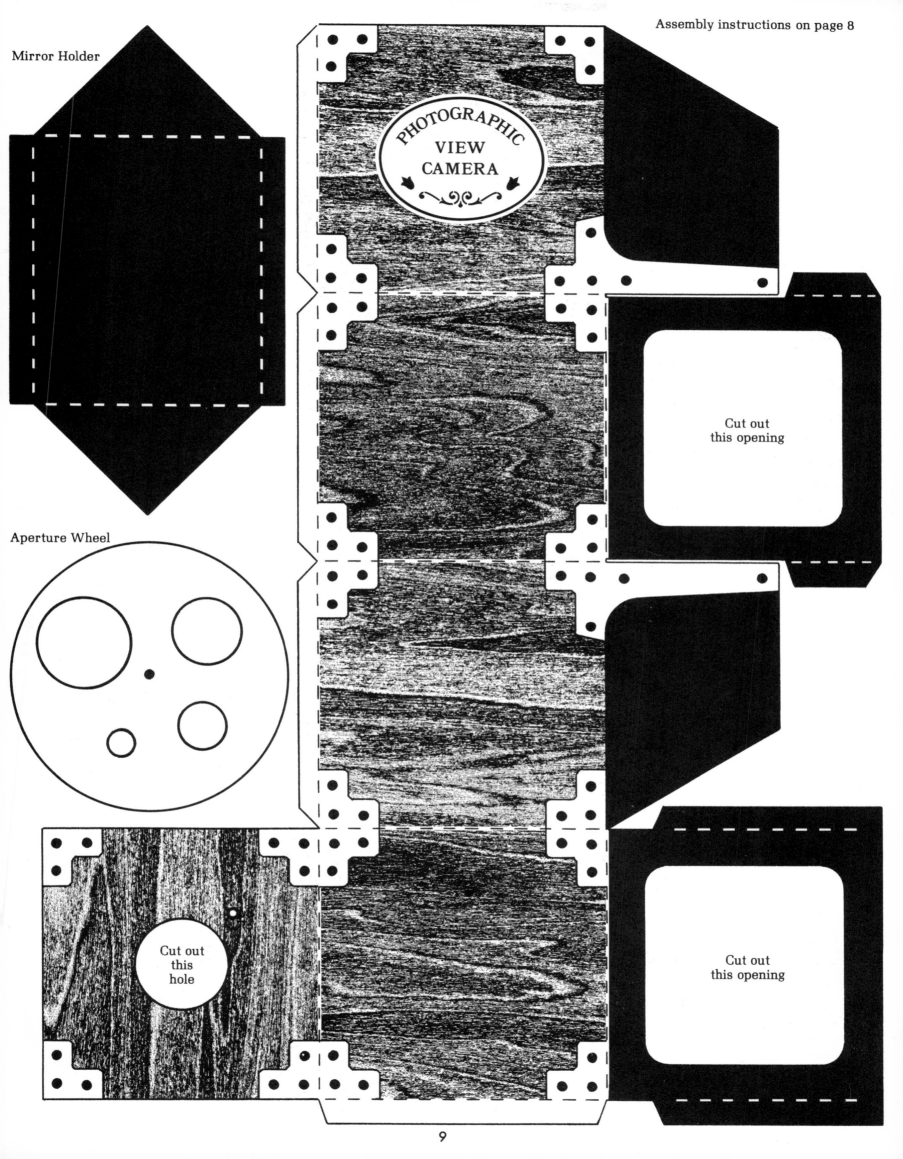

Mirror Holder

Aperture Wheel

PHOTOGRAPHIC
VIEW
CAMERA

Cut out
this opening

Cut out
this
hole

Cut out
this opening

Official Daguerreotype CAMERA with rear mounted mirror for upright viewing. (George Eastman House)

PHOTOGRAPHIC VIEW CAMERA

Since ancient times, people have known that certain materials change colors when left in sunlight. As a rather strange example, the early Romans dyed their robes with mucous from purpura snails which turns bright purple after a day in the sun.

In 1816 a French inventor named Nicephore Niepce made a discovery. He coated some paper with the light-sensitive chemical, silver chloride, and placed it in a camera obscura. When he aimed this device out a window for several hours, the light which focused on the paper slowly darkened it, to create an exact duplicate of the scenery outside — the world's first photograph. The camera obscura he used had become the world's first CAMERA. Niepce's first pictures no longer exist, because the paper continued to darken after it was removed from the CAMERA. Later Niepce teamed up with Louis Jacques Daguerre, who in 1839 revealed the now-famous Daguerreotype process, recognizable today as mirror-like images on silver coated copper plates.

Instructions for building your VIEW CAMERA are on page 8. To operate, simply aim it out a window and hold a magnifying glass in front of the aperture (hole). Move the lens back and forth, until in just the right position a bright clear picture pops into focus on the viewing screen. Try different hole sizes by rotating the aperture wheel. To view the picture right side up, set a mirror in the holder at the back of the camera and look in the mirror.

To take pictures, use "studio proof paper" from a camera shop instead of film. This paper darkens naturally in bright light, much like the first photo papers that Niepce used. No chemicals are needed to develop the picture. Support the camera and magnifying glass on a table and aim out a window as shown, using modeling clay or styrofoam to hold the lens. After you focus, insert a piece of the photo paper, shiny side facing the lens, in front of the viewing screen. Wait 5 or 10 minutes and presto, you have a picture.

Suggestions: Try different exposure times. Do this on a sunny day, but don't let sunlight hit the camera when photo paper is in it. Store your pictures in a dark container to keep them from darkening more. The following papers work almost as well: Velox, Kodabromide, Brovira, Kodabrome RC, or Ilfobrome. Polycontrast papers do not work well for this project.

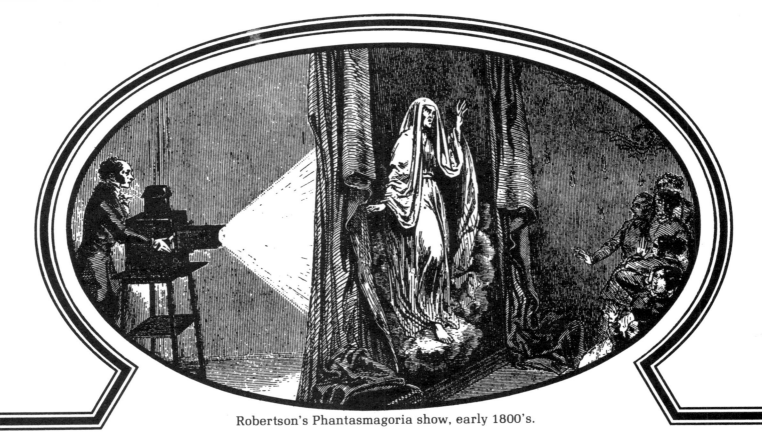

Robertson's Phantasmagoria show, early 1800's.

MAGIC LANTERNS by Johann Zahn, 1685.

MAGIC LANTERN

The great-grandparent of our modern day slide projector is the MAGIC LANTERN. To operate your cut-out model from pages 13-16, shine a flashlight or small desk lamp in the back end; put a slide in the holder; and position a magnifying glass in front as shown. Move the lens to focus. In a very dark room, you'll be surprised how well it works.

The first MAGIC LANTERNS, dating back to around 1660, were used almost exclusively by priests and magicians to conjure up images of ghostly demons and evil spirits. These shows were the predecessor of our modern monster movies. It was all done with candles and lenses. But so horrifying was the experience to the unknowing audiences that they often screamed for mercy and even fainted from terror. Images projected onto billowing clouds of smoke appeared to dance about or even jump out at people. The famous projectionist Robertson chose just the right setting for his "Phantasmagoria" show, as it was called — an old abandoned monastery, late at night.

The ready-to-make MAGIC LANTERN.

To make a
MAGIC LANTERN projector

1. Cut, fold and glue like this:

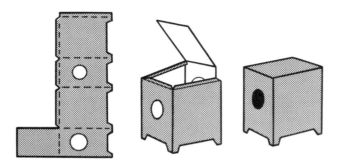

2. Next assemble and glue the smoke stack from page 15 as shown.

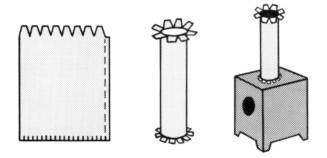

3. The slide holder from page 15 glues on like this:

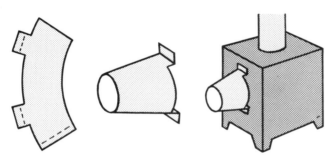

Page 12 tells how to operate the Magic Lantern. Page 14 suggests slides to use with this project.

Magic Lantern

Cut out this hole

Slide Holder here

Slide Holder here

Magic Lantern

Glue smokestack here

Cut out this hole

Do not use with candle or flame

Where to get slides for your
MAGIC LANTERN

1. Ask family and neighbors for extra 35mm slides — they fit nicely in this projector.

2. Or, make slides of cardboard this size, and tape old negatives in them.

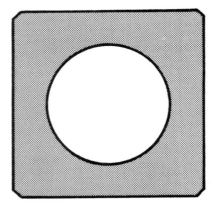

3. To use the old-fashioned lantern slides from page 15, trace the round drawings onto clear plastic with a waterproof, fine-tip marking pen. Then cut out the holes and tape the plastic drawings in their place.

4. Make extra slides of your own design using clear plastic and cardboard.

5. Pictures can be scratched onto stiff, clear plastic using a sharp instrument such as a large needle or the point of a compass. Color them with a water-proof felt pen.

Smokestack

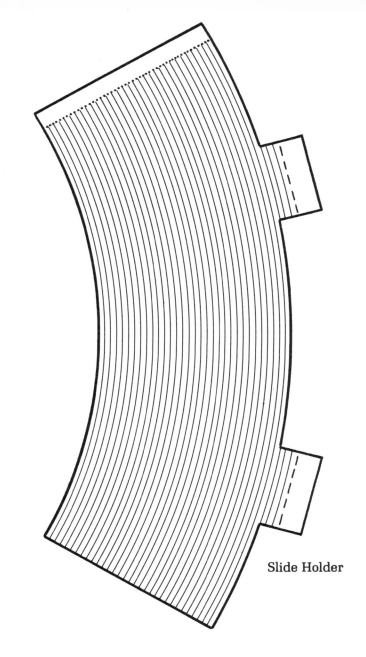

Slide Holder

Gulliver's Travels Series   Millikin & Lawley Co., London, 1890

Adapted from Lantern slide by M. Lefevre, 1830, French.   (Universal City Studios collection)

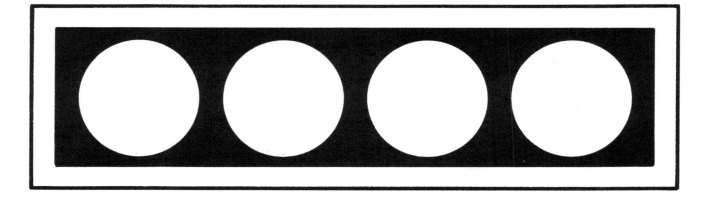

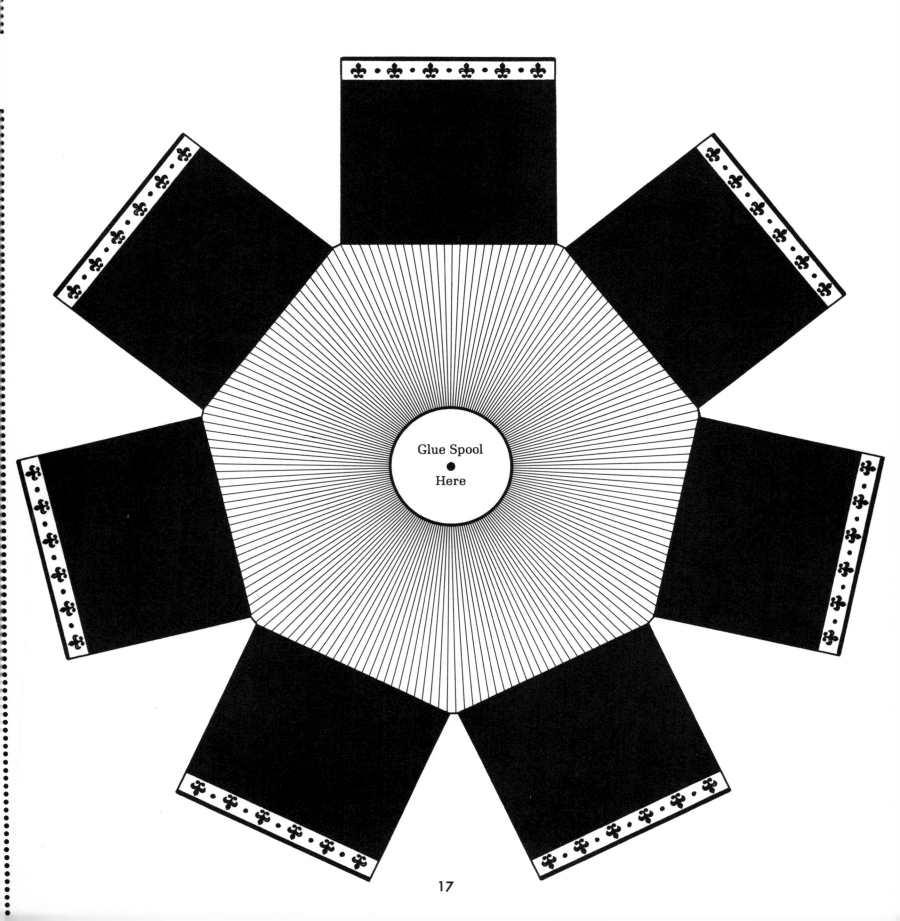

Glue Spool

Here

How to make a
ZOETROPE

1. Cut out the piece below and tape like this, with the pictures facing in. Be sure to *leave spaces* between the side sections, about this wide:

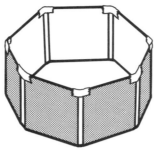

2. Find a spool that turns easily on a pencil, and glue it to the bottom.

To operate the ZOETROPE, spin it on the end of a pencil and look through the *slits* — the pictures will come to life.

ZOETROPE · SINCE 1834

18

MOTION PICTURE MACHINES

Motion picture history started with a whole variety of strange looking machines that all worked by showing a series of pictures in rapid sequence. The human eye is too slow to notice the gap between pictures. The cut-out gadget on page 18 is a type of ZOETROPE, most popular of the early movie toys.

This invention was first made by an Englishman in 1834, and again in France in 1860, where it was manufactured in large numbers. But another seven years later the famous American toy manufacturer, Milton Bradley, siezed on the idea and was granted a patent in the United States as the inventor of the ZOETROPE!

Toward the end of the nineteenth century, experimenters too numerous to mention combined the features of the magic lantern with the ZOETROPE to create projected motion pictures. From their work the movie industry was born. All the apparatus used in exhibiting motion pictures had incredible sounding names, but the prize must certainly go to the one which most accurately described its purpose — the "Getthemoneygraph"!

Optical Toys for the Holidays.
ZOETROPE.

The ZOETROPE, or "Wheel of Life," is an instructive Scientific Toy, illustrating in an attractive manner the persistence of an image on the retina of the eye; it consists of a card-board cylinder, about 12 inches diameter, and 8 inches deep, with 18 equidistant narrow openings, each about 3 inches long, arranged near the top as shown in the engraving. The lower end rests on an iron shaft, rising from a substantial wood base; on strips of paper, about 3¼ inches wide, 36 inches long, are printed figures of men, animals, etc., in different positions, which are placed in the cylinder. By revolving the cylinder by the hand, and looking through the openings, the images passing rapidly before the eye are blended, so as to give the figures the motions of life in the most natural manner. As many persons as can stand around the Zoetrope can see the movements at the same time.

PRICE OF THE ZOETROPE, $2.50.

T. H. McALLISTER, OPTICIAN, 49 NASSAU STREET, N. Y.

(Zoetrope advertisement courtesy of N.M. Graver)

First of the movie toys, invented 1832.
(courtesy of S.F. Fine Arts Museums and Ron Slaughter)

An early attempt at "filming" people in motion, by E.J. Marey, 1882.
(Gernsheim collection, University of Texas)

DIORAMA

An unusually well-crafted DIORAMA for home use.
(courtesy of Larry Edmunds Book Shop, L.A.)

Today we think of a DIORAMA as a large museum display filled with stuffed animals and creative scenery. But originally the word meant an optical system for viewing special paintings, illuminated either from the front or the rear, for changing effects and mood.

You can build your own DIORAMA using the cut-outs on page 21. Watch the scene change from night to day by opening and closing the flaps in just the right way, as shown at the left.

This device, first invented in 1811 in Switzerland, reached its peak with French partners Bouton and Daguerre. They set up elaborate exhibition theaters in Paris and London, displaying DIORAMIC paintings over four stories high and nearly twice as wide. To change scenes, the entire seating section was rotated. People tossed wads of paper at the pictures to see if the scenery was real.

DIORAMA theaters sprang up everywhere, and so great was the craze that a whole new slang developed along with it. A friend of yours might ask, "How's your healthorama today?"

An original DIORAMIC scene, showing the change from day to night.
(courtesy of Universal City Studios)

FRONT LIT

BACK LIT

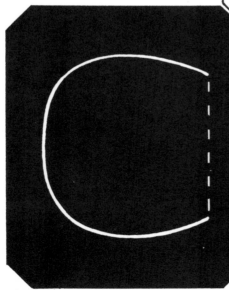

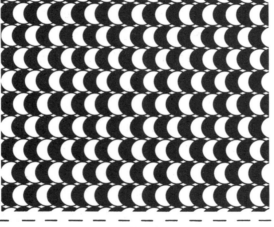

How To Make a DIORAMA

1. Cut, fold and glue as shown.

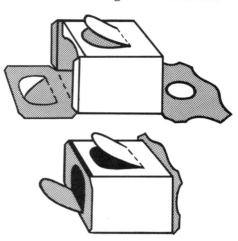

Do not glue along the section marked like this:

****

2. Put tabs of folded tape on the two flaps to make them easier to open and close.

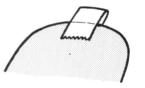

3. Cut out the three pictures and make tiny pin holes where you see the white dots.

To operate, slide a picture into the rear slot that was left un-glued, and look through the peep hole toward a light. Open one flap as you close the other to alternate between night and day.

Cut out
this
hole

DIORAMA

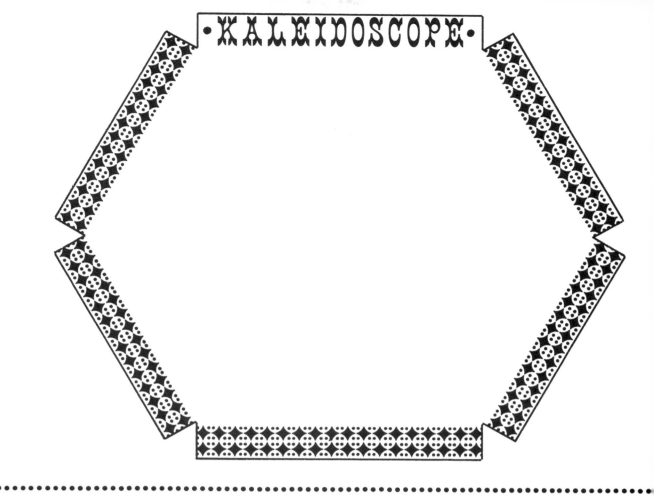

·KALEIDOSCOPE·

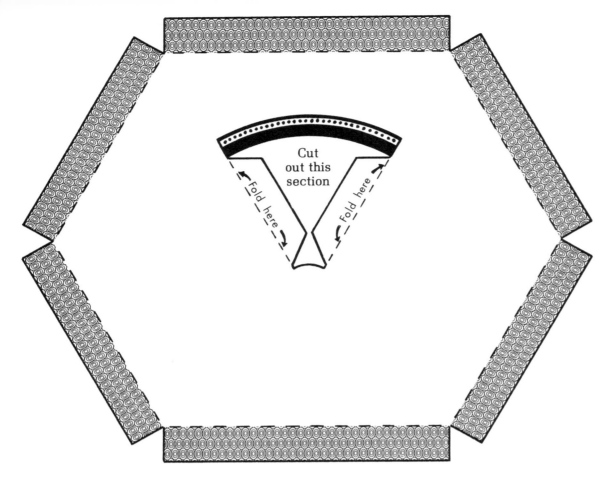

Cut out this section

Fold here

Fold here

1. Cut out the piece at the left; fold and tape the sides like this:

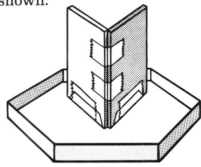

2. Tape two purse size mirrors together, and then fasten them to the base with tape as shown.

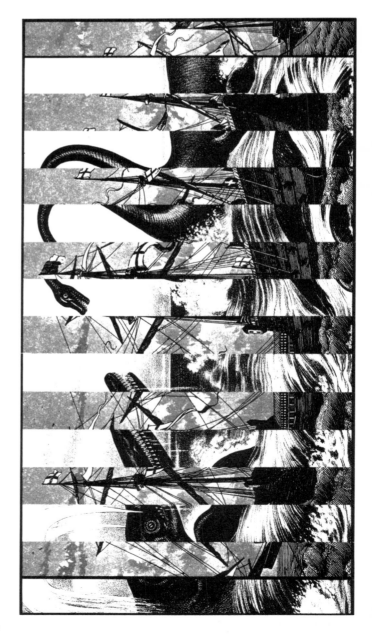

Page 25 tells how to operate the KALEIDOSCOPE.

KALEIDOSCOPE

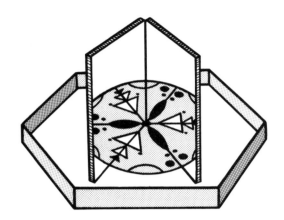

Original 19th Century KALEIDOSCOPE
(Universal City Studios Collection)

The KALEIDOSCOPE, still popular throughout the world today, was an instant success soon after its invention by David Brewster in 1816. Anyone who peered into the magical tube, was captured for hours by the endless variety of beautiful, changing patterns reflected by the mirrors concealed inside.

You can make a KALEIDOSCOPE by following the instructions on page 24. Your completed model, shown above, is operated by sliding it over brightly colored images such as comic strips, wrapping paper, photographs, or the cover of this book.

BISCENEORAMA

A fashionable wall decoration for nineteenth century parlors was the BISCENEORAMA (bi-scene-o-rama) which showed two different pictures, depending on where you stood. Construction is simple — just score and fold the cut-outs on page 24 like the folding pattern shown here. Magic pictures having three different scenes were also popular but a bit more complicated to fold. The descendents of these old-time folded pictures are the plastic changing picture buttons that people wear today.

From *Popular Scientific Recreations*, by Tissandier.
(Dr. Martin Perl collection)

FOLDING PATTERN

Left eye   Right eye

Wheatstone's 3-D drawings
and first STEREOSCOPE, 1832.

STEREOSCOPE

Take a look at the pictures on the left, and notice that the drawings for each eye are slightly different. Then glance at some objects nearby using one eye at a time. You'll agree that the eyes do see two views of things, because of their spacing on your head. This idea of bilateral vision has been known for 2000 years, but not until 1832 did inventor Charles Wheatstone use it to add the illusion of depth to flat surface drawings.

To view a three-dimensional (3-D) scene you need two separate pictures and a viewer that comfortably allows each eye to view each picture independently. The most popular variety of STEREOSCOPE for this purpose is shown at the right. And of course, the camera needs two lenses spaced just like the eyes on your head.

Like the kaleidoscope before it, the STEREOSCOPE was hailed as the "optical wonder of the age." People could sit by the fireside and peek into the far reaches of the globe, without ever suffering the risk or expense of actually going there. No Victorian home was complete without one.

The operation of the cut-out STEREOSCOPE from page 27 is shown below. You will be viewing one picture directly and the other by reflection in a mirror. Look through the eyeholes in the direction of the arrows. Then shift the mirror around slightly until the double image you see blends into one, and suddenly the scenes will pop into 3-D. It takes a little experimentation at first, but once you've got the idea, its easy.

STEREOSCOPE and 3-D camera. (Bingham Museum of Photography, University of Cal. at Riverside, photo by John Kleinman)

1. Cut, fold and glue the piece on the lower left like this:

2. Cut and fold the piece at the right and glue it to the first piece.

3. Tape a mirror on like this, using tape wherever necessary.

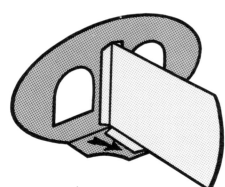
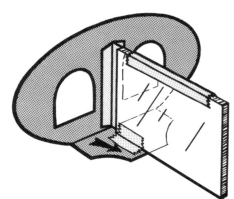

Page 26 tells how to use the STEREOSCOPE.

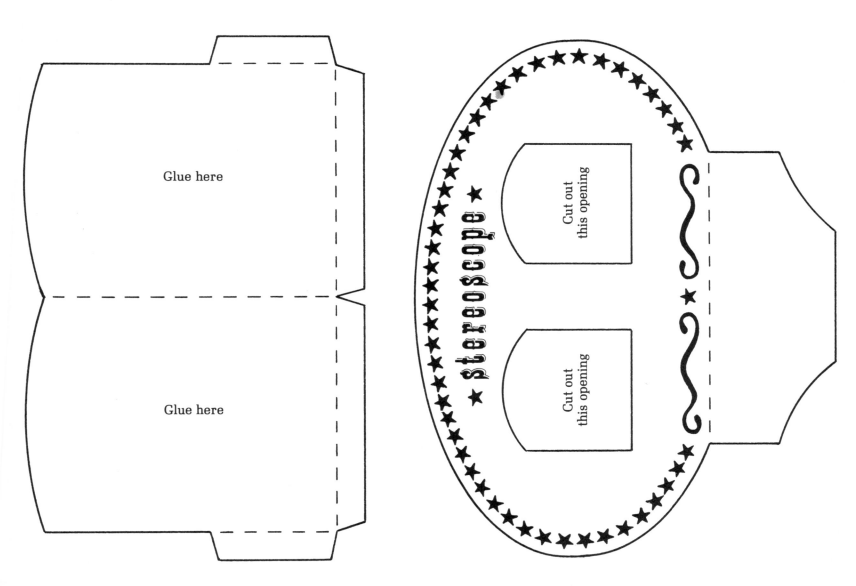

Glue here

Glue here

★ stereoscope ★

Cut out this opening

Cut out this opening

**Getting his Hair Banged
Keystone View Company, 1897**

The stereo view cards on the next two pages may be cut apart, or if you prefer, they will work just as well bound in the book. The extra cards on the back cover should be left intact to help protect the guide book that remains.

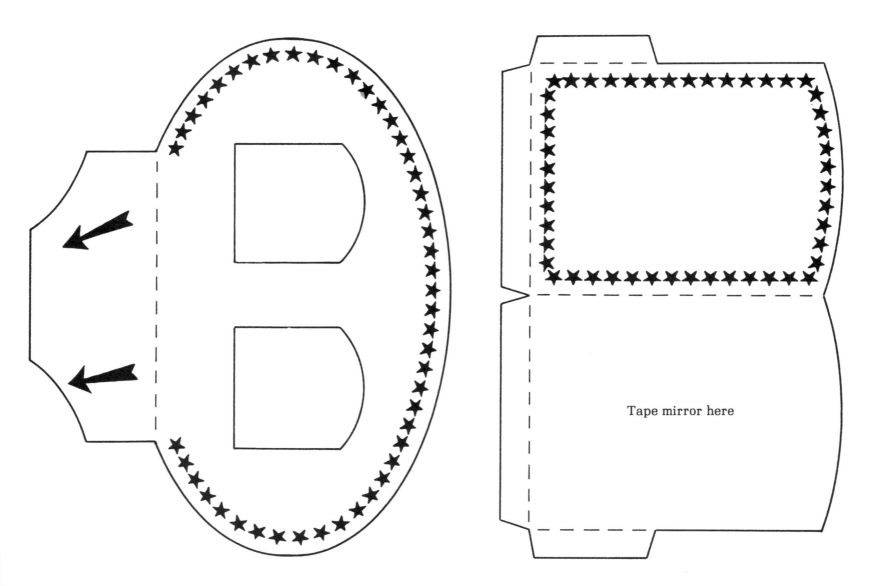

Tape mirror here

STEREO VIEWS FROM AROUND THE WORLD

Bathing in the Sacred Ganges
Benares, India
Keystone View Company, c.1910

Horseshoe Falls in Winter
Niagara, N.Y., U.S.A.
H.C. White Company, 1902

Derby Day
Epsom Downs, England
Keystone View Company, c. 1900
(courtesy of Ralph Elliott)

(San Francisco Cliff House scene on back cover,
courtesy of Ralph Elliott)

In the Heart of Box Canyon
Colorado, U.S.A.
Keystone View Company, 1897

A Well-tended Japanese Garden
Keystone View Company, 1904

An Ostrich is Born
Underwood & Underwood, 1898